Heaven Must Be Full of Balloons

Written by Nancy Toothaker

Cover Design by Keith Barrows

Back Cover Design by Karen Heath

Co-Illustrated by Keith Barrows and Karen Heath

Heaven Must Be Full of Balloons by Nancy Toothaker is a wonderfully personal story that memorializes the life of her son. It also addresses in a clear and poignant manner the issues faced by children who lose a parent. It gives concrete ideas for helping children grieve, in a Christian context. It addresses some issues, such as problems encountered with other children at school, which other books of this nature often ignore. I highly recommend this book as a useful tool for grieving children.

Rachel Baker, LMHC
Family Support Counselor and
   Former Grief Counselor
Big Bend Hospice

Heaven Must Be Full of Balloons is wonderfully written from the heart. Nancy Toothaker wrote this story with the help from other family members and it is a reflection of the love that continues after the death of someone. The book offers an insight into the life of a man who was a son, a father and a husband. It allows the person who died to continue to be a loving part of a family through shared memories from different stories told by his mother and his children. As adults read this story to their children it may encourage them to start sharing their own memories and stories. A useful book for both adults and children.

Rosey Ilic, MSW
Grief and Loss Counselor
Big Bend Hospice

Only God knows the hurting of the hearts of the children left to face life with so many questions of why. Only God can wrap his loving arms around that hurting heart and dry the tear from a child's eyes. This book is very special and I pray that God will use it greatly.

Larry Myers
Mexico Missionary

About the Author

Nancy Toothaker was born and brought up in Winchendon, Massachusetts and has resided in Tallahassee, Florida for 25 years. She is a mother of four, grandmother of seven and great-grandmother of two who adores children and loves to write. Her prayer is that this book will be a comfort to little ones everywhere who have suffered a loss.

About the Illustrators

Keith Barrows is a college graduate with a degree in Environmental Science. Keith is married and has two daughters. He has lived in Winchendon, Massachusetts most of his life and considers this his home. His talent for art comes from his love to draw for others.

Karen Heath is a mother of two, grandmother of two, and although having lived in Florida 13 years, considers Mississippi her home. She has been a nurse for 25 years and though very rewarding, her artwork has been her passion.

In Loving Memory of
Randy Scott Toothaker

God gave us a sweet
small boy
To love and care for and to
bring us joy

And though these treasures
we no longer see
Deep within our hearts
he will always be

This book is dedicated to

Randy's wife Noal

His daughters Katherine and Janie

His sisters and brother Tammy, Kel and Rick

His nieces and nephews

Sarah, David, Jake, Ashley and Megan

and his father Ron

Special Thanks

Special thanks to my granddaughter Sarah for all her help in the setting up and display of this book. Her knowledge of computers far surpasses mine and she generously gave all the time needed to complete my dream.

Special thanks to my grandson David who (unbeknownst to him) came up with the title of this book. On the fourth of July eleven family members went to the cemetery and with love and in remembrance of Randy's 33rd birthday released thirty-three red, white, and blue balloons, a beautiful sight as they soared heavenward. When we were leaving Randy's grave site David looked up at me and said, "Heaven Must be Full of Balloons!"

Note to Parents

Sometimes Daddies and Mommies die when their children are very young and still need them so very much. Understanding why a Daddy or Mommy is here today and gone tomorrow is one of the most difficult tragedies to explain to a child. We have to try and help them understand why Daddy or Mommy is no longer here to swing them up on a shoulder, play hide and seek, listen to their prayers, tuck them in bed at night and just to be there. They need to know that Daddy or Mommy didn't choose to leave and how much he still loves and misses them.

It is my hope that this book will help children see that they can show their love to their missing parent in their own special way – they can still say, "I love you and miss you." They also need something concrete to hang onto, something they can physically touch. Balloons seem to fill that need as they can send them to their missing loved one.

My granddaughters hug their balloons, give them a kiss and send them off saying, "I love you Daddy."

As two little girls cope with the death of their Daddy,
they learn more of his young life.

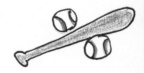

The fireworks were bursting in the night sky, the moon was smiling and the stars were twinkling brightly when a beautiful baby boy was born one fourth of July. His Mommy and Daddy named him Randy. His two sisters and brother could hardly wait for him to arrive home. They were so excited to see their new baby brother. They hugged him, kissed him and held him so tight when his Mommy and Daddy brought him home. He had golden hair and the most beautiful smile. The days went by so fast before they knew it he was walking and talking.

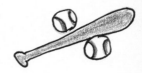

Randy had so many animal friends. He had lots of fun playing with puppies, kittens and

even bunnies. One of his favorite day trips was going to the pond to feed the ducks.

Even snakes were his friends.

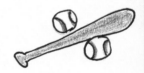

Randy loved the colorful butterflies that came to visit all the flowers. He

laughed and played with them. They flew round and round him and

sometimes landed on his finger and stayed to visit for awhile.

When spring arrived the front lawn of Randy's home was always covered with bright

yellow dandelions. It was his favorite time of year. He would stoop down in a sea of

bright yellow flowers choosing the prettiest and brightest ones to bring to his Mommy.

As he handed those dandelions to her the big grin on his face matched the happy smile

his Mommy gave to him. She opened her arms wide and gave him a big hug and said, "I

love you, Randy."

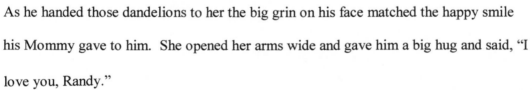

The precious flowers were placed in a special vase on the kitchen window sill where the

sun shined through the window and made them look bright and beautiful. Mommy

enjoyed them so much.

Randy was a gentle boy who loved picking flowers for his Mommy, but he also liked playing hockey, baseball, and football. His hip was injured one day while playing football and after a trip to the doctor's office, he had to pack his suitcase and head off to the hospital for a while until his hip got better.

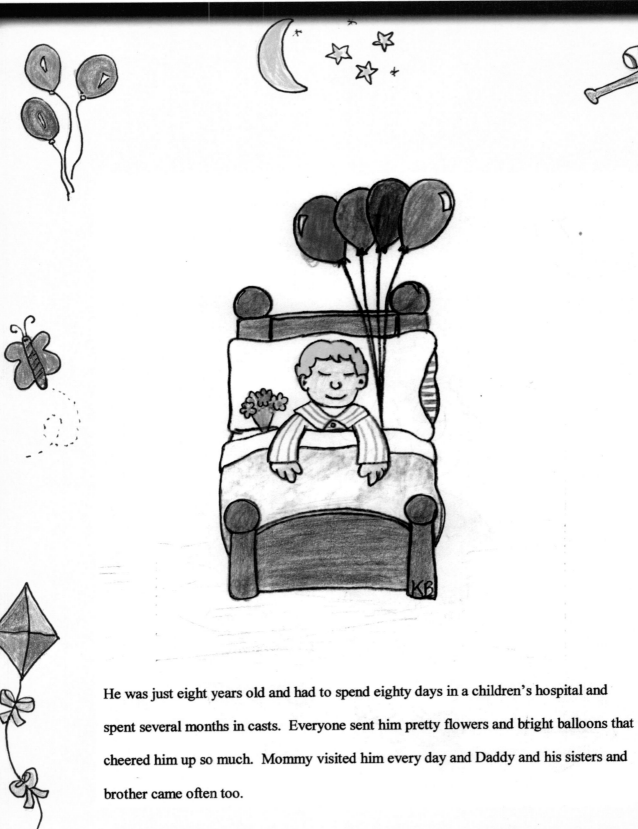

He was just eight years old and had to spend eighty days in a children's hospital and

spent several months in casts. Everyone sent him pretty flowers and bright balloons that

cheered him up so much. Mommy visited him every day and Daddy and his sisters and

brother came often too.

He and his friends at the hospital raced up and down the hallways in their special wheelchairs. One day the boys ran into Nurse Smily and were grounded for the remainder of the week. They remembered to be more careful the next time they were allowed to drive.

Daddy built Randy his own red cart with his name on it. It had big wheels like a wheelchair so he could make it go wherever he wanted. It supported the heavy casts that were on both of his legs. He even played baseball from his cart. His sisters and brother loved playing ball with him.

When he was in a body cast, one night his brother Rick took him to a friend's home to visit. Rick and Mark decided to take a short-cut home so they would get there before dark. There was lots of snow and Randy's red cart hit a bump. Randy went sailing off his cart and landed in a snow bank. His frightened brother Rick ran to him. As Randy looked up from the cold snow bank he had landed in, he was smiling. He laughed and said it was fun sailing through the air and landing in a soft snow bank. Rick and Mark lifted him onto his cart but had to carry him and the cart home as the accident had ripped the front wheel right off his special red cart. Randy grew stronger every day and before he knew it a year had passed. He was so happy when the last cast was removed and he was home to stay.

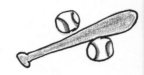

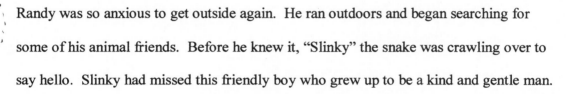

Randy was so anxious to get outside again. He ran outdoors and began searching for some of his animal friends. Before he knew it, "Slinky" the snake was crawling over to say hello. Slinky had missed this friendly boy who grew up to be a kind and gentle man.

When he grew up he met a very special girl. They loved each other very much and were married in a beautiful little chapel. It was a perfect summer day and pretty flowers were blooming all around. They were pink and purple and smelled so sweet. It was a lovely wedding and they were so happy.

After a few years they had a beautiful baby girl who they named Katherine and two years later a little sister named Janie came into the family. They thanked God everyday for their precious little girls. Daddy loved to play with them and tickle them and make them laugh. They giggled and squealed and had so much fun.

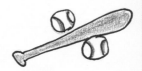

Just before listening to their prayers and tucking them into bed at night Daddy would

bring them out to see Mr. Moon and all the twinkling stars shining so brightly in the sky.

Katherine and Janie always waved and said, "Goodnight Moon." When they were all

snuggled in their beds, Daddy and Mommy would often read them stories of Jesus and

His love.

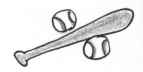

One cold and rainy day in March their Daddy became very sick. His mom, Nannie, took him to the hospital. After a short time Mommy joined Daddy and Nannie there. They stayed with him every moment. Later that day he whispered, "Please tell my sweet girls I love them so much." Daddy was too sick to come home and a few hours later he went to be with Jesus.

The sound of beautiful music filled the air as the angels came to escort their Daddy to Heaven where everything is beautiful and no one is ever sick. The streets are made of gold, the angels are always singing and everyone is happy forever and evermore.

After Daddy died there was a funeral at the church and there is a stone with his
name on it right near the chapel. All of his family visit there and bring pretty
flowers. On Easter Sunday Katherine and Janie brought a basket of eggs they
had colored for Daddy. There is a birdhouse hanging in the tree and baby
chickadees were born there. It's very pretty at Daddy's special place.

KB

Katherine saw her Daddy many times after he died. She would exclaim to Mommy,

"Can't you see Daddy?" "He's right there!" as she pointed to a certain spot. "He has red

and orange wings, and he told me he loves me and Janie," she said with a big smile on

her face.

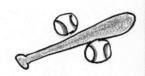

One sunny day little Katherine said, "Mommy, I miss my Daddy." "Could he come to visit us for just a little while?" Mommy answered, "He can't come to see us here, but you can send him a balloon to let him know how much you love him and miss him." Katherine smiled brightly and said, "I want to send him a red one!" and Janie can send him a blue one. And that night when they fell asleep they dreamed of their Daddy's big smile when he reached out and caught the red and blue balloons filled with their love.

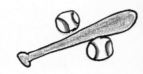

A short time after Daddy went to Heaven Mommy made a "Daddy Book" for
Katherine and Janie. This was a book filled with pictures of Daddy holding
them, going to special places, and just having fun together. Their "Daddy
Book" is so special. Katherine and Janie look at all of these fun pictures
almost every day. They know Daddy loves them very much.

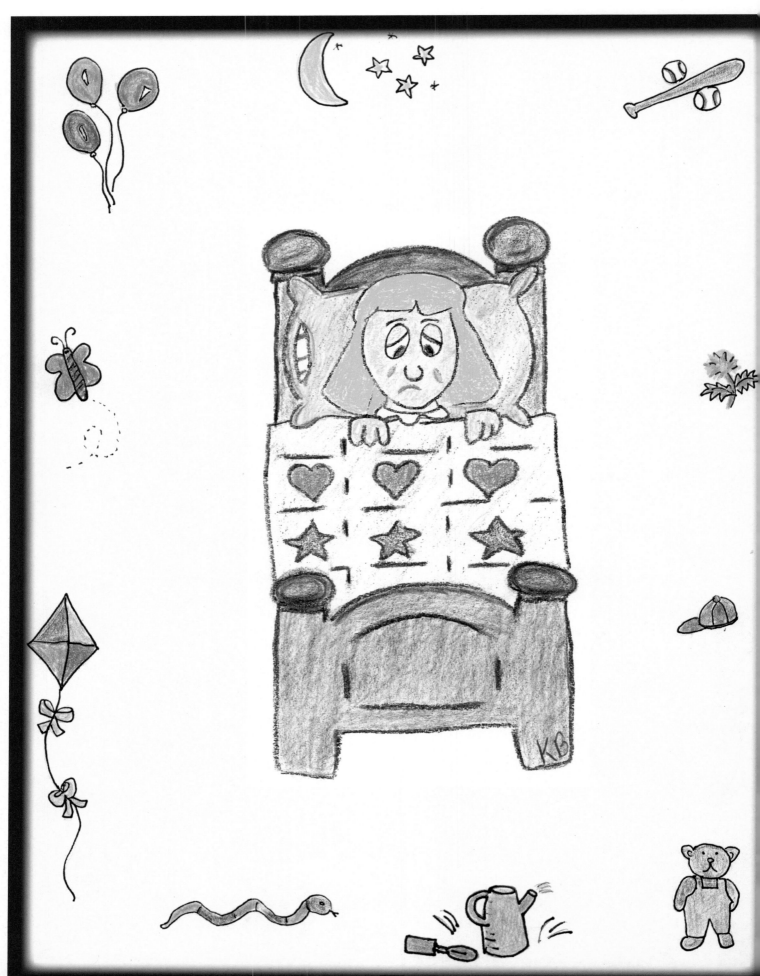

Not long after her Daddy died and Katherine was missing him, she wanted to take her Cozy teddy bear to bed. He was yellow, Katherine's favorite color, and so soft and huggable. Cozy couldn't be found anywhere and Katherine announced that he was lost. She was so sad and cried for her Cozy. She cried very hard and said to her Mommy, "My Cozy's gone forever just like my Daddy." "Why did my Daddy die?" Katherine cried harder and harder. She was very upset.

Mommy hugged Katherine tight and gently explained that Daddy still loved her even though he wasn't here to tell her. "I will help you search for your Cozy," Mommy said. Many telephone calls were made to both of her grandmothers', her cousins', and friends' homes to see if Cozy had been left at one of these places. Everyone was searching for Cozy, and at last he was found in a far corner of Daddy's closet. Katherine held her Teddy high in the air and called out excitedly, "Mommy, I found Cozy!" She hugged him tight and said to Mommy, "it's like giving Daddy a hug." I love Daddy and Cozy!

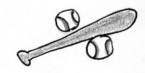

One morning at pre-school Miss Kelly reminded all the children to bring their daddies to school the next day as it was "Donuts for Dads" day. Katherine stood up and announced, "My Daddy can't come; my Daddy died." She was sad and also angry that her Daddy wouldn't be able to come.

When Katherine got home from school that day, she told Mommy that she didn't like it one bit that her Daddy had gone away and couldn't be with her at "Donuts for Dads" or any other time. "It's not fair, Mommy," declared Katherine! "All my friends have daddies, "she said with a tear in her eye. Mommy explained that sometimes Daddies die. They don't want to. They just do. "Daddy still loves you and Janie very much. He will always love you."

Baby Janie grew so fast it seemed no time and she was in pre-school too. Little Janie

came home from pre-school one day and began crying. Big tears rolled down her cheeks

as she told Mommy that some of the kids at school had chanted, "Janie doesn't have a

Daddy." Mommy gave Janie a big hug and held her close for a long time; and Mommy

told Janie that the other children just didn't understand. "Of course you have a Daddy; he

is in Heaven and he loves you very much." We can't see him but we can feel his love.

Janie immediately went to Daddy's closet and pulled one of his big shirts over her head.

It went down to her ankles. She slipped her tiny feet into Daddy's big shoes. As she

clomped around the house in the oversized shoes and shirt , she sang, "My Daddy's in

Heaven and he loves me."

One Spring day Janie was about to leave Nannie's house to go to a birthday party when a cool breeze began to blow. She shivered and said, "I'm cold." Nannie smiled and went to her closet and came back with a small yellow hooded jacket – just Janie's size. She told her that it was her Daddy's jacket when he was a little boy. Janie giggled as she slipped into the jacket that fit perfectly and remarked – "My Daddy was "THIS" little!" Then she happily skipped off to the birthday party in the precious yellow jacket that Daddy once wore.

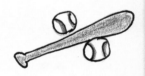

It was a special day when Katherine and Janie planted a tree in Nannie's back yard in memory of Daddy. They dug and planted and watered and had a wonderful time. They named their tree "The Daddy Tree" and they often go out by the tree when they send balloons to Daddy.

It was a beautiful Valentine's Day as Katherine and Janie headed for Nannie's back door with two balloons to send to Daddy. As they opened the back door they were surprised to see two heart-shaped balloons tied to the "Daddy Tree." No one knew who had tied the balloons to the tree. Katherine and Janie put their heads together and suddenly it was like a light bulb came on in their heads and they both said, at the same time, "Daddy sent them!" Later, Nannie explained to the girls that she had a dream and in it Daddy had smiled and said "I would love to send balloons to my girls. They have sent so many to me." So Nannie made sure there were two special balloons tied to the "Daddy Tree" on Valentines Day.

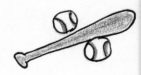

Sending balloons became a family tradition. On his birthday, the fourth of July, many family members and several friends went to Daddy's special spot and released thirty-three red, white and blue balloons; and oftentimes on special days his two little girls and all the other children who love him so much send balloons filled with love to him. As their balloons fly high into the sky soaring heavenward, one can often hear the words, "Heaven Must Be Full of Balloons!"

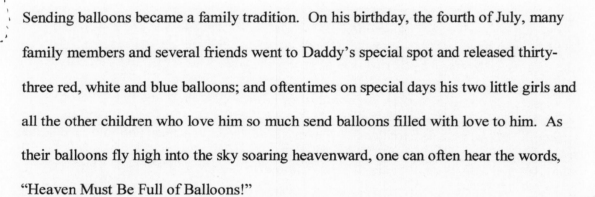

To my children

"LOVE IS A DANDELION BOUQUET"

Have you ever received a gift so sweet
As when he toddled in on tiny feet

With hands clasped tight behind his back
A look of love he does not lack

His eyes shine bright with joyful glee
As he hands his precious gift to me

Though children know not the flowers from the weeds
Much love is sown from these small seeds

His glorious gift of innocent love
Surely comes from Heaven above.

God sent these messengers of love to me
And each day I give thanks to Thee

There comes a time when they are grown
With lives to manage on their own

When problems come into each life
And times for each are full of strife

I'd gladly give up life you see
If problem free their lives could be

"I don't make deals my dear
But I am always ever near"

"They know you're there
They know you care"

"Please let go and trust in Me
They need My help to clearly see"

Because I love them so
It's so hard to let them go

And though the fragrance of the flowers is no longer there
I know they're in the hands of a loving God who will always care.

I love you

Mom

"RANDY'S SHOES'

Black or white or red or blue
In a corner, on a chair I'd often find a little shoe

They would run and jump and skip and play
One small pair of shoes each day

When he was just a little mite
His hockey skates I tied so tight

Dressed from head to toe in hockey gear
He played the game for just a year

For at the tender age of eight
Encased in plaster was his fate

For several months in bed he lied
His special shoes I often tied

When that great ordeal was done
His precious shoes again did run

As he grew so strong and tall
Tennis seemed to be his call

He played the game precisely and with zest
It was the companionship and friendship he liked best

When his years neared thirty-three
I tied his shoes on bended knee

He was sick as sick could be
One more time he needed me

His precious days on earth are done
No more shoes my precious son

Escorted to Heaven by angels sweet
He needs no shoes upon his feet

Forevermore with Jesus he will be
And again one day his precious face we'll see

So when the tears upon my face still glisten
It is to a still small voice I listen

No more have I a tear-stained face
When I seek God's sustaining grace

I love you Randy
Mom

"DADDY'S LITTLE ANGELS"

His first little angel came into his life
Five years after his sweetheart became his wife

She had a head full of silken-like hair
Her cheeks were so rosy, her skin was so fair

Her tiny hand curled around his finger so tight
Right then he gave his heart to this sweet tiny mite

There never was a doubt that right from the start
Her handprint was forever sealed in his heart

His tears fell like rain one morning at dawn
As his thoughts drifted to the day his sweet angel was born

He fell to his knees and whispered a prayer
I'll tell her of Jesus while she's in my care

Time passed so quickly-soon two years were gone
It was then that his second angel was born

Blessed with another angel form Heaven above
This baby girl filled their lives with much love

She reached out and touched him and captured his heart
She cooed and she smiled; he was hooked from the start

He now had two angels, one on each side
Forever in his heart they will always abide

He adored being Daddy and gave them much love
Way too soon he was called home to Heaven above

Katherine and Janie miss their Daddy so much
They miss his sweet kisses and his soft gentle touch

They now have a guardian angel of their very own
To love and watch over them till God calls them home

He has wings of bright orange and red
That's what his first-born Katy-Did said
And little Jane-Bug agreed with a nod of her head

Closing

Remembering our loved ones in a special way helps so much. The first birthday that Randy was not with us, his thirty-third on the fourth of July, was still celebrated with a birthday cake in loving memory of him. We all went to the cemetery and released thirty-three red, white and blue balloons. Everyone felt closer to him. The week before Christmas we take a little Christmas tree to his grave site. Katherine, Janie, Sarah and David all get so excited when the time draws near. We decorate the tree together. Each one has his or her own special ornament that she or he has chosen to remember him in a special way. His sisters and brother and nieces Ashley and Megan from out of state send ornaments they have chosen to hang on his tree. As we hang them on the tree feelings of love abound. He always has lovely silk flower arrangements for each season of the year and fresh flowers are placed at his grave site often. Angels are on either side of his headstone and a small statue of a boy and his dog sits close by. A birdhouse hangs on the tree that stands beside his headstone. A Mama chickadee laid her eggs in the birdhouse this past spring and three baby birds greeted us one day when we visited. Chimes hang in the tree along with sun catchers. His resting place looks so pretty. Randy is loved, missed and remembered always. Heaven is a beautiful place where we can all be someday where there are no more tears or hurts and there is love, peace, joy and happiness forever and ever. Trusting Jesus is our hope. Life must go on for the living. Not a day goes by that I do not long to see Randy, hear his voice and his laughter and see his beautiful smile. I do know that one day we will be reunited and those gifts will once more be mine to enjoy. Randy no longer has to see through a glass darkly. He is in God's glorious light with Jesus.